What do you call a one-eyed Dinosaur?

Other books in this series:

What Wears a Sock on its Bottom?

How Do You Make a Skeleton Laugh?

What Happens When the Queen Burps?

Poetry Collections by John Foster:

School's Out

Excuses, Excuses

Football Fever

I've Got a Poem For You

Poetry by John Foster:

The Poetry Chest

What do you call a one-eyed Dinosaur?

Rip-roaring jokes, riddles, and rhymes selected by John Foster

Illustrated by Mark Oliver

OXFORD
UNIVERSITY PRESS

OXFORD
UNIVERSITY PRESS

Great Clarendon Street, Oxford OX2 6DP

Oxford University Press is a department of the University of Oxford.
It furthers the University's objective of excellence in research, scholarship,
and education by publishing worldwide in

Oxford New York

Auckland Cape Town Dar es Salaam Hong Kong Karachi
Kuala Lumpur Madrid Melbourne Mexico City Nairobi
New Delhi Shanghai Taipei Toronto

With offices in

Argentina Austria Brazil Chile Czech Republic France Greece
Guatemala Hungary Italy Japan Poland Portugal Singapore
South Korea Switzerland Thailand Turkey Ukraine Vietnam

Oxford is a registered trade mark of Oxford University Press
in the UK and in certain other countries

The selection and arrangement © John Foster 2013
Illustrations © Mark Oliver 2013

The moral rights of the author and illustrator have been asserted

Database right Oxford University Press (maker)

First published 2013

British Library Cataloguing in Publication Data
Data available

ISBN: 978-0-19-275740-1

1 3 5 7 9 10 8 6 4 2

Printed in Great Britain

Paper used in the production of this book is a natural,
recyclable product made from wood grown in sustainable forests.
The manufacturing process conforms to the environmental
regulations of the country of origin

CONTENTS

DINOSNORES AND DINOSTORIES

What do you call a one-eyed dinosaur?
A do-you-think-he-saw-us.

What do you call a one-eyed dinosaur's dog?
Do-you-think-he-saw-us-Rex.

What do you call a sleeping dinosaur?
A dinosnore.

What do you call a dinosaur that is not very clever?
A dopelodocus.

How did dinosaurs pass their exams?
With extinction.

What do you call a dinosaur that never gives up?
A try-try-try-ceratops.

What do you call an ugly dinosaur?
An eyesore.

What do you call a nervous dinosaur?
Tyrannosaurus Wreck.

What do you call a dinosaur who's always on time?
A Pronto-saurus.

What do you call a dinosaur that takes part in rodeos?
A Bronco-saurus.

The Do-you-think-he-saurus
There's a do-you-think-he-saurus
Been along this track before us.

Do you think he saw us,
The do-you-think-he-saurus?
And if he thinks he saw us,
Will he just ignore us,
The do-you-think-he-saurus?

Do you think he will explore us,
The do-you-think-he-saurus?
Do you think he'll scratch and claw us?
Do you think he'll crunch and gnaw us,
The do-you-think-he-saurus?

There's a do-you-think-he-saurus
Been along this track before us.

HOW DOES A SPACE MONSTER HOLD UP ITS PANTS?

How does a space monster hold up its pants?
With an asteroid belt.

What do you call a monster with no neck?
The Lost Neck Monster.

What has pointy ears and lives in a lake in Scotland?
The Spock Ness Monster.

How does Frankenstein's monster sit in a chair?
Bolt upright.

What monster lives in Scotland and never
wins the lottery?
The Luckless Monster.

Has anyone seen the Abominable Snowman?
Not Yeti.

Why did Frankenstein's monster get indigestion?
Because he bolted his food.

Beware!
Beware of . . .

the elastic monster—it'll try to stretch you
to the limit.

the rope monster—it'll try to tie you up in knots.

the ironing monster—it'll try to flatten you.

the electric monster—it'll try to give you a shock.

the eraser monster—it'll try to rub you out.

the mop monster—it'll try to wipe the
floor with you.

the screwdriver monster—it'll try to turn the
screw on you.

the computer monster—it'll try to delete you.

Knock, knock.
Who's there?
Turner.
Turner who?
Turner round very slowly. There's a monster
behind you.

Knock, knock.
Who's there?
C.D.
C.D. who?
C.D. monster out here with me? Open up or
he'll break the door down.

WHY DOES A GIRAFFE HAVE SUCH A LONG NECK?

Why does a giraffe have such a long neck?
Because it can't stand the smell of its feet.

Why are some snakes good at sums?
Because they are adders.

Why wasn't the flea chosen for the football team?
Because he wasn't up to scratch.

What does a lion press most on his DVD player?
Paws.

What was the spider
doing on the computer?
Searching the web.

I Play Games with My Cheetah
I play games with
    my cheetah,
But I can never beat her,
Because my cheetah's a
    cheater.

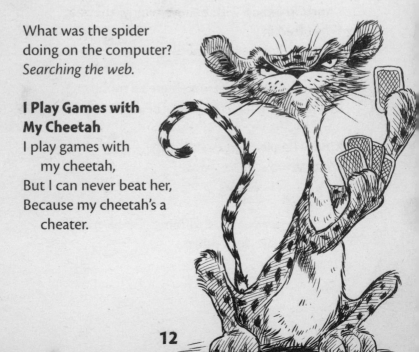

12

Animal Complaints

'I'm just a dogsbody,' complained the dog.
'What about me? I do the donkey work,' replied
    the donkey.
'Don't be such an ass,' interrupted the pig.
'I'm the one who has to give piggy-backs.'
'You're pig-headed,' squawked the hen.
'At least you're not henpecked.'
'Well I am,' retorted the horse.
'I'm not allowed to indulge in any horseplay.'
'And I have to take care not to slip on any cowslips,'
Moaned the cow.
'Every night someone insists on counting us,'
Bleated the sheep sheepishly.
'And I'm fed up with being a nanny,' the goat
    butted in.
Meanwhile, the bull dozed.

Thunder and Lightning

Thunder and lightning rent the air
And all the world was shaken.
The little pig leapt from his sty
And ran to save his bacon.

I LOVE ALL MY TEACHERS

I Love All My Teachers
I love all my teachers
from my head down to my belly.
I love to do my homework
even though I miss the telly.
I love to do detention
and I love to stay up late,
revising for my tests,
'cause I think teachers are great.
They're kind and smart and helpful,
they're delicate and gentle.
And I am—yes, you've guessed it—
absolutely mental.

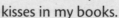

Darren: I think my
teacher loves me.
Emily: Why?
Darren: She puts lots of
kisses in my books.

Deborah Delilah

Deborah Delilah, she liked a bit of fun.
So she went to Tesco's and bought a currant bun.
Deborah Delilah—what a naughty creature—
Dipped the bun in treacle and threw it at her
   teacher!

Smart Alec

Teacher: How do you spell wrong?
Smart Alec: R-o-n-g.
Teacher: That's wrong.
Smart Alec: That's what you asked for, isn't it?

Teacher: Alec, if you had four pounds in one
pocket and six pounds in another pocket,
what would you have?
Smart Alec: Someone else's trousers on.

Teacher: Give me a sentence starting with 'I'.
Smart Alec: I is . . .
Teacher: No, Alec, you must always say 'I am'.
Smart Alec: Oh, right. I am the ninth letter
of the alphabet.

Teacher: What word, if pronounced right is
wrong, but if pronounced wrong, is right.
Smart Alec: Wrong.
Teacher: Right.

Teacher: Who discovered electricity?
Smart Alec: Some bright spark.

Teacher: Can you tell me Napoleon's nationality.
Smart Alec: Course I can.

A Gym Teacher Who Came from Quebec
A gym teacher who came from Quebec,
Wrapped both of his legs round his neck.
I'm afraid he forgot
How to untie the knot
And now he's a highly-strung wreck.

SHARK! THE MERMAID ANGELS SING

Shark! The Mermaid Angels Sing
Shark! The mermaid angels sing
What presents will Christmas bring?
Shipwrecked sailors, fishermen,
Guide them to our lair again,
Where we'll enchant them with our charms
And keep them captive in our arms.
Shark! The mermaid angels sing
What presents will Christmas bring?

Good King Wenceslas

Good King Wenceslas looked out,
In his pink pyjamas,
Sliding down the banisters
Eating ripe bananas.
Brightly shone the screen that night
On the television
While he watched the late night film
Instead of doing revision.

While Shepherds Watched the Match that Night

While shepherds watched the match that night
On their home computer,
A flash of lightning made it crash
And they could not reboot her.

And so they missed the game that night
And did not know the score
Till the angel of the Lord came down
And said it was a draw.

Violent Night

Violent night! Violent night!
The reindeer all
Have taken fright.
Lightning flashes

And thunder roars.
So hold on tight,
Please, Santa Claus
Or there'll be no presents tonight!
There'll be no presents tonight!

TOO MANY CLICKS SPOIL THE BROWSE

Proverbs for the Computer Age
Surf, chat and be merry for tomorrow
you may catch a virus.

Too many clicks spoil the browse.

What boots up must close down.

It's no use crying over lost files.

It is better to have searched and failed
than never to have searched at all.

The e-mail of the species is much faster
than the mail.

Don't byte off more than you can view.

There's many a true e-mail sent in error.

To err is human, but to really mess things up requires a computer.

You can't teach an old mouse new clicks.

Gigabyte Giggles
What is a cursor?
A person who swears at a computer when it doesn't do what they want it to do.

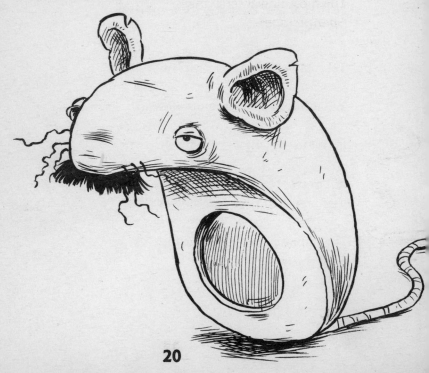

What made the computer scream?
Someone stepped on the mouse.

What do dolphins use computers for?
To send each other sea-mails.

Which is the best website in the animal kingdom?
The Onlion King.

Why was the computer in pain?
Because it had slipped a disk.

In which European city do people receive
the most unwanted e-mails?
Spamsterdam.

MY FIRST IS IN BLOOD AND TWICE IN UNDEAD

Simply the Best
At bloodsports Dracula
Is reputed to be spectacular.

Riddle Me a Count
My first is in blood and twice in undead.
My second is in nightmare and also in dread.
My third is in fangs but is not in doom.
My fourth is in coffin but not in tomb.
My fifth's in bloodsucker but not in vein.
My sixth's in bloodcurdling, and in bloodstain.
My last is in vampire but not in bite.
I rise from my grave on the stroke of midnight!
(answer on page 93)

The Grand Old Count of York
The Grand Old Count of York
He had ten thousand bats.
He kept them in his wardrobe
Hanging from his cloaks and hats.
And when he went out they flew out
And when he went in they flew in
And when they were neither in nor out
They haunted his neighbours' flats.

Advert from *The Vampire Weekly*

Dracula—Your Questions Answered

Why is Dracula's bank account always in the red?
Because it is in a blood bank.

Who does Dracula always take to a party?
The girl necks door.

Who did Dracula invite to his wedding?
All his blood relatives.

What does Dracula say before going out?
I'm just popping out for a bite.

What pets does Dracula own?
A bloodhound and a ghoulfish.

What kind of letters does Dracula get from admirers?
Fang mail.

Why did the art teacher praise Dracula?
Because he was good at drawing blood.

The Vampire's Apology

'I didn't mean to cause offence,'
Said the vampire with a grin.
'But when I saw you'd cut your face,
I just had to lick your chin!'

The Friendly Vampire

'Come in,' the friendly vampire said.
'There's room in my tomb for two.
Together we'll have a late-night bite
And I'll share my drink with you!'

The man shook his head.
'I'd rather be dead!'
The vampire gave a grin.
He took a peck
At the poor man's neck
And greedily sucked him in.

Knock, Knock

Knock, knock.
Who's there?
Adair.
Adair who?
Adair you to open
this door and see my fangs.

COUNT'S CASTLE, TRANSYLVANIA

For the holiday of a lifetime, stay at Count's Castle, Transylvania. Whatever your blood group, you can be sure of a warm welcome from the Count and his staff.

- Visit the Crypt Bar where you can sample the full range of our renowned red wines.
- Relax and have a full neck massage at our Suckers Spa.
- Swim at midnight in our infamous Red Pool, then take a romantic moonlight stroll in our graveyard.
- Evening entertainments include songs from Snarl and the Werewolves and you can dance the night away in our Zombies disco to music from Lucifer and the Sharptooths.
- Or simply while away your last hours in the Veins cinema, watching the latest fangtastic vampire movies, before enjoying a final meal in our Bloodsuckers restaurant.

CHILDREN UNDER TWELVE STAY FREE

FREE HOLIDAYS

at full moon for young vampire enthusiasts, including nightly Kids Club with activities in Batty Bat's Cave and a spine-chilling ride through Dracula's Dark Dungeon.

NIGHTMARES GUARANTEED!

Terms and Conditions: For our safety, all visitors will be searched at reception and any stakes, crosses, or garlic will be confiscated and destroyed. Full details of our latest offers can be found at the Transfusion Tours website.

WHAT DID ONE TOILET ROLL SAY TO ANOTHER?

What did one toilet roll say to another?
I can't tear myself away from you.

Why did Tigger keep sticking his head
down the toilet?
He was looking for Pooh.

26

What did the bath say when he thought
the toilet was ill?
You're looking flushed.

What do you call a woman with two toilets
on her head?
Lulu.

What vegetables do you find in toilets?
Peas and leeks.

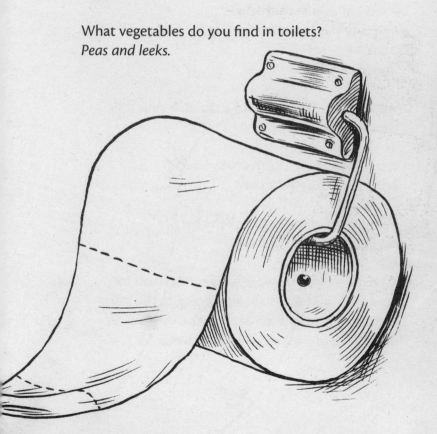

If Your Toilet Seat is Broken

If your toilet seat is broken,
Whatever you do,
Don't try to mend it
With superglue.

Don't Wait

If you wake up in the night
And your bladder's feeling tight,
Don't wait
Until it's too late.

What do you do if you find a snake in your toilet?
Wait until it's finished.

Why did the baker have smelly hands?
Because he kneaded a poo.

Mummy, Mummy, can I lick the bowl?
No, flush it like everyone else.

'I am married to a sewage worker. My small son, aged four, pulls the chain after going to the toilet and announces with pride that it's on its way to Daddy.' (*From a letters page in a newspaper.*)

Newsflash

Going Quietly

When a ptarmigan goes to the loo,
He makes less noise than you or I do.
The reason is plain, you see,
He has a silent p.

On the Throne

The King sat on his throne,
Doing what he had to do.
Then he pulled the chain
And the courtiers bowed
As he flushed the royal loo.

YOU CAN'T TUNA FISH

What's the Difference...?
What's the difference between the law and
an ice cube?
One is justice and the other is just ice.

What's the difference between a fish and a piano?
You can't tuna fish.

What's the difference between see and sea?
You can see the sea, but the sea cannot see you.

What's the difference between ignorance
and apathy?
I don't know and I don't care.

What's the difference between a boxer and
a man with a cold?
One knows his blows and the other blows his nose.

What's the difference between Prince Charles
and a javelin?
*One is heir to the throne and the other is
thrown in the air.*

What's the difference between a butcher
and an insomniac?
One weighs a steak and the other stays awake.

What's the difference between someone who is
desperate for the lavatory and someone who is
trapped in the lions' enclosure?
One is dying to go and the other is going to die.

What's the difference between a musician
and a corpse?
One composes and the other decomposes.

What's the difference between a wizard
and the letters M A K E and S?
One makes spells and the other spells 'makes'.

What's the difference between a teacher
and a train?
*One says, 'Take that gum out of your mouth,'
and the other says 'Choo choo.'*

What's the difference between a nail and a boxer?
One gets knocked in and the other gets knocked out.

What's the difference between a well-dressed
man and a dog?
A well-dressed man wears a suit, a dog just pants.

What's the difference between a weasel and a stoat?
*A weasel's weasily recognized, but a stoat's
stotally different.*

What's the difference between a spider and an
internet hacker?
*One uses a web to trap bugs off a log and the other
uses a web to log in and bug people.*

COCKAPOODLEDOOS AND DASH-HUNDS

What dog is always in a hurry?
A *dash-hund.*

What do dogs call parking meters?
Pay toilets.

What do you get if you cross a cocker spaniel
with a poodle and a rooster?
A *cockapoodledoo.*

Our dog's really lazy.
Why do you say that?
Yesterday, I was watering the garden and
he never lifted a leg to help me.

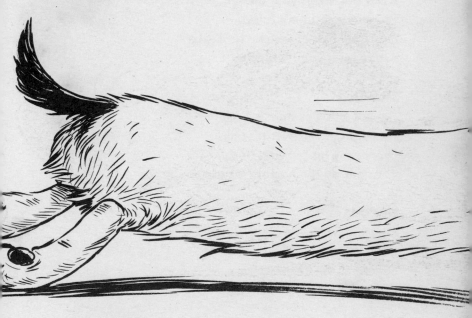

Newsflash

**FORTY PEDIGREE DOGS HAVE
BEEN STOLEN FROM SOME KENNELS.**
A police spokesman said they have no leads.

Why are dogs such bad dancers?
They have two left feet.

If Our Dog Steals Your Dinner

If our dog steals your dinner,
Pretend you do not mind.
Don't tell him off, or else he'll take
A bite from your behind.

Thin Dog

I've got a dog as thin as a rail,
He's got fleas all over his tail;
Every time his tail goes flop,
The fleas on the bottom all hop to the top.

Our Dog

Our dog has fused the Christmas lights.
He went up to the tree,
Sniffed at the decorations,
Cocked his leg and did a wee.

Maggie's Shaggy Dog

There was a young lady called Maggie,
Whose dog was enormous and shaggy;
The front end of him
Looked vicious and grim—
But the back end was friendly and waggy.

'My dog can read,' boasted a boy to his friend.
'How do you know?' asked his friend.
'Yesterday, it saw a sign saying WET PAINT, so it did.'

Two owners were arguing over whose dog
was the cleverest.
'My dog is so smart,' says the first owner, 'that every
morning he waits for the paper boy to come round.
He tips the boy then brings the newspaper to me,
along with my morning coffee.'
'I know,' says the second owner.
'How do you know?'
'My dog told me.'

Suzie was given two dogs which she called Rolex
and Timex. 'Where did you come up with those
names?' asked her friend Linda.
'Oh, that was easy,' replied Suzie. 'They're both
watchdogs.'

What do you call a cross between a dog
and a phone?
A golden receiver.

Two dogs were walking down the road. One dog says to the other, 'Wait here a minute. I'll be right back.' He walks over to a lamppost, sniffs it for about a minute, then returns to his friend. 'What was that all about?' asks the other dog. 'Just checking my messages.'

What happened when the dog went to the flea circus?
He stole the show.

ASK AN EASY QUESTION, GET A SILLY ANSWER

Game Show Gaffes
Game Show Host: When you have completely misunderstood the question, you are said to have got hold of the wrong end of the what?
Contestant: Dog.

Game Show Host: In science, what is botany the study of?
Contestant: Bottoms.

Game Show Host: How many leaves are there on a four-leaf clover?
Contestant: Three.

Game Show Host: Name an animal with really good sight.
Contestant: A bat.

Game Show Host: Name something made out of wool.
Contestant: Sheep.

Game Show Host: According to the common saying, revenge is a dish best served—what?
Contestant: On toast.

JUMBO JETS AND ELEPHANTOMS

Why are elephants difficult to catch?
Because they're elusive.

What do you call a well-dressed elephant?
Elegant.

What do clever elephants study at college?
Electronics.

How do elephants travel long distances?
By jumbo jet.

Which lost city are elephants always looking for?
El Dorado.

How do psychic elephants communicate?
By elepathy.

What do you call an elephant that is out of breath?
An elepant.

What type of schools do young elephants go to?
Elementary schools.

What do you call an elephant's ghost?
An elephantom.

How do elephants greet each other?
They bellow 'ello.

Why is it hard to understand what some
elephants say?
They speak mumbo jumbo.

Why do elephants never win competitions?
They are always eliminated.

How do elephants feel when they win a
prize in a raffle?
Elated.

What do you get when an elephant sits
on your best friend?
A flat mate.

Why do elephants have Big Ears?
Because Noddy wouldn't pay the ransom.

Eletelephony
Once there was an elephant
Who tried to use the telephant—
No! No! I mean an elephone
Who tried to use the telephone—
(Dear me! I am not certain quite
That even now I've got it right.)

Howe'er it was, he got his trunk
Entangled in the telephunk;
The more he tried to get it free,
The louder buzzed the telephee—
(I fear I'd better drop this song
Of elephop and telephong!)

GEOGRAPHICAL GIGGLES

Q. What are the Mediterranean Sea and the Red Sea joined by?
A. The Sewage Canal.

Q. Why is Wales sinking into the sea?
A. Because there are so many leeks in the ground.

Q. What was the largest island before Australia was discovered?
A. Australia.

Q. What's the capital of France?
A. F.

Q. What do you find in the middle of Egypt.
A. The letter 'y'.

Q. What do you call the small rivers that run into the Nile?
A. Juveniles.

Long-legged Italy

Long-legged Italy
Kicked poor Sicily
Right in the middle
Of the Mediterranean Sea.
Austria was Hungary
Took a bite of Turkey
Dipped it in Greece
Fried it in Japan
And ate it off China.

Mississippi Said . . .

Mississippi said to Missouri,
'If I put on my New Jersey,
What will Delaware?'
Virginia said, 'Alaska.'

Geographical Definitions

A reef is a knot of coral.
A down is a soft covering of hair growing on a
grassy upland.
A peak is a glimpse of a mountain summit.
A plateau is a high level of flattery.
A geyser is an old bloke spouting forth.
A gully is a cricketer fielding in a small valley.
A headwind is a polite term for a belch.
A meander is a boy and girl strolling along a
riverbank.

Teacher: Can anyone tell me where Ben Nevis is?
Smart Alec: He's not in this class, sir.

Teacher: Where are the Great Plains found?
Smart Alec: At the great airports, sir.

SEARCH ME

Answers on page 93

Find the Letter

1. What is in the church, but not in the steeple?
   The parson has it, but not the people.

2. What's in the ceiling, but not in the floor?
   The cupboard has it, but not the drawer.

3. What's once in awhile, but not in time?
   It's there in ascend, but not in climb.

4. What's in the bassoon, but not in the drum?
   It's not in your fingers, but there in your thumb.

5. What's there in bread and also in bake?
   The biscuit has it but not the cake.

6. What's there in werewolf, but not in wizard?
The python has it, but not the lizard.

7. Which two letters spell 'chilly'?

8. What is the laziest letter?

9. Which is the most inquisitive letter?

10. Which two letters spell 'rot'?

11. What is the beginning of eternity,
The end of time and space,
The beginning of every end;
At the end of every race?

12. What is never out of sight,
Occurs twice in a season,
Comes once in first,
In second and in treason.

LET THIS BE A WARNING TO YOU

Colin Crete—A Cautionary Tale
Colin Crete would drink and eat
From morning until night.
He filled his mouth so full of food
It was a horrid sight.

He shovelled up his food so fast
It wouldn't all fit in,
So bits of it were hanging out
And dripping down his chin.

One day he stuffed his mouth so full
He could not move his jaw.
Try though he might for one last bite,
He fell down on the floor.

The doctor came and looked at him.
He sadly shook his head.
'Poor Colin choked on all that food.
And I'm afraid he's dead.'

So do not be like Colin Crete.
Whatever else you do,
Eat just enough and do not bite
Off more than you can chew.

A Disappearing Act

I didn't believe the magician
When he said in a voice loud and clear
That for his final trick
He'd make someone disappear.

So I volunteered at once
To be shut in a metal box
While he wrapped chains around it
And secured it with several locks.

Then he tapped on the box with his wand
And uttered a magic spell
And I felt my whole body shaking
As into the darkness I fell.

I found myself back in my seat
From where I was able to see
The magician open the box
To show there was no sign of me.

All around me the people were clapping
And giving the magician a cheer
While I sat there wondering when
He would make me reappear.

Now everyone's left and gone home.
The magician has left the stage too
And I am sitting here waiting
And wondering what I can do.

Which is why I strongly advise you
Never to volunteer
To be the person that a magician
Says he will make disappear.

A Big Mistake

My owner's made a big mistake.
He thinks I'm not a poisonous snake.
I'm waiting till the time is right
To give him just a tiny bite.
To let him know a snake like me
Should not be in captivity.

CRAZY CREEPY CRAWLIES

What's the difference between a maggot
and a cockroach?
Cockroaches crunch more when you eat them.

Why was the insect told to leave the park?
It was a litterbug.

What do you call a beetle in a spacesuit?
Bug Lightyear

When did the fly fly?
When the spider spied her.

What is the definition of a snail?
A slug with a crash helmet.

What do you call a baby ant?
An infant.

Did you hear about the angry flea?
He was hopping mad.

What do you get if you cross a flea with a rabbit?
Bugs Bunny.

Why was the glow-worm sad?
Because her children weren't very bright.

What happened when the two silkworms
had a race?
It ended in a tie.

Earwig Jo
The ants and the earwigs were having a football
match. The ants were winning one–nil. At the end
of the first half the manager of the earwigs told Jo,
'Get warmed up, you're playing.' By full time Jo had
scored ten goals and all the fans were chanting,
'Earwig Jo! Earwig Jo! Earwig Jo!'

What's the Hurry?
Two ants were racing as fast as they could across
the top of a box.
'Hey!' puffed one ant. 'What's the hurry? Why are
we running so fast?'
'Can't you read?' said the other. 'It says here, tear
along the dotted line.'

BATTY BOOKS BY APTLY NAMED AUTHORS

An A–Z of Letters by Alf A. Bet.

A Guide to Tattooing by Marcus Allover.

The Runaway Bull by Gay Topen.

Cooking Made Easy by Mike Rowave.

A Flaw in the Law by Lou Pole.

CHAOS! by May Hem.

Desperation by Fran Tic.

This Land Is My Land by Terry Tory.

I Did It My Way by Ed Strong.

Blowing Hot and Cold by Luke Warm.

SERVING IN THE ARMY by Reggie Ment.

Information Brochures by Pam Flets.

A Frog's Life by Lily Pond.

Successful Cueing by Bill E. Yards.

Quick as a Flash by Millie Second.

VERSE BY VERSE by Stan Za.

Quick Snacks by T. N. Biskits.

HOLE IN MY BUCKET by Lee King.

DEAD FUNNY

Jumping to a Conclusion
There was an old man who averred
He had learned how to fly like a bird;
Cheered by thousands of people,
He leapt from the steeple—
This tomb states the date it occurred.

The Greedy Man
Here lies a greedy man called Chester
Who ate a whole goose, but could not digest her.

Passed Away
He passed the lorry without any fuss,
And he passed the cart of hay.
He tried to pass the swerving bus
And then he passed away.

Epitaph for John Bun
Here lies John Bun.
He was killed by a gun.
His name was not Bun, but Wood.
But Wood would not rhyme with gun
But Bun would.

Never Say Die

Old burglars never die—they just steal away.
Old police officers never die—they just cop out.
Old gamblers never die—they go to the dogs.
Old librarians never die—they turn over a new leaf.
Old surgeons never die—they cut and run.
Old footballers never die—they kick off.
Old lawyers never die—they close their briefcases.

Why are there fences around cemeteries?
Because people are dying to get in.

HITTING THE HEADLINES

Headlines You Could Have Seen

SOMETHING WENT WRONG
IN JET CRASH, EXPERT SAYS.

IF STRIKE ISN'T SETTLED QUICKLY,
IT MAY LAST A WHILE.

MINERS REFUSE TO WORK AFTER DEATH.

Astronaut Takes Blame For Gas In Spacecraft.

POLICE FOUND SAFE UNDER BLANKET.

LATECOMERS MISS START.

ARTIFICIAL LIMBS CENTRE HAS NEW HEAD.

WOMAN IS SHEEP DOG CHAMPION.

YOUTH HIT BY TRAIN IS RUSHED TO TWO HOSPITALS.

Ex-Boxer Battered Outside Chip Shop.

BUS ON FIRE—PASSENGERS ALIGHT.

And Ten Headlines You Won't Have Seen

Theatre Burglar Steals the Show.

SANTA'S HELPERS GIVEN THE SACK.

SWORD SWALLOWER HAD
A POINT TO MAKE.

FANS GIVE TV STAR A WINDY RECEPTION.

VEGETABLE SHOW JUDGES IN A PICKLE
OVER ONIONS.

TATTOOED FOOTBALLER GIVEN A FREE TRANSFER.

SOAP STAR MAKES A CLEAN BREAK.

PURSUING PHOTOGRAPHER
MADE A SNAP DECISION.

Successful Window Cleaner Takes a Step Up.

PEOPLE FORCED TO GO ELSEWHERE
BY TOILET CLOSURE.

KNOCK, KNOCK—IT'S FREEZING OUT HERE!

Knock, knock.
Who's there?
Twitter.
Twitter who?
I didn't know you did owl impressions.

Knock, knock.
Who's there?
Ammonia.
Ammonia who?
Ammonia little boy. I can't reach the doorbell.

Knock, knock.
Who's there?
Eider.
Eider who?
Eider let me in or I'll climb through the window.

Knock, knock.
Who's there?
Chuck.
Chuck who?
Chuck the key under the door and I'll let myself in.

Knock, knock.
Who's there?
Will.
Will who?
Will you please hurry up? It's freezing out here.

Knock, knock.
Who's there?
Howl.
Howl who?
Howl you know unless you let me in?

Knock, knock.
Who's there?
Teller.
Teller who?
Teller to turn off the TV and come and
open the door.

Knock, knock.
Who's there?
Repeat.
Repeat who?
Who, who, who ,who . . .

DON'T SPIT ON THE FLOOR

The Old Man of Darjeeling
There was an old man of Darjeeling
Who boarded a bus bound for Ealing.
It said on the door,
'Don't spit on the floor'
So he stood up and spat on the ceiling.

There Was a Young Lady Called Harris

There was a young lady called Harris
That nothing would ever embarrass
Till the salts that she shook
In a bath that she took
Turned out to be plaster of Paris.

The Old Lady from Clyde

There was an old lady from Clyde
Who ate forty apples and died.
The apples fermented
Inside the lamented
And made cider inside her insides.

There Was a Young Man from Porthcawl

There was a young man from Porthcawl
Who went to a fancy dress ball
Dressed up like a tree,
But he failed to foresee
His misuse by the dogs in the hall.

A Mouse in Her Room Woke Miss Dowd

A mouse in her room woke Miss Dowd;
She was frightened and screamed very loud,
Then a happy thought hit her
To scare off the critter,
She sat up in bed and meowed.

The Old Man From Vancouver

There was an old man from Vancouver
Whose wife was sucked into the Hoover.
He said, 'There's some doubt
If she's more in than out,
But whatever it is I can't move her.'

A Young Schoolboy Called Chris

There was a young schoolboy called Chris
Who said, 'Ignorance is bliss
And what you don't know
Can't hurt you, so
I think I'll give homework a miss.'

RIDDLE ME A RIDDLE

Answers on page 93

1. I'm inside a whistle and inside speak.
I'm found in a pod and a mountain's peak.

2. What has a neck, but not a head
And sits on a bar or a shelf,
Wearing a metal or plastic cap
That it cannot remove itself.

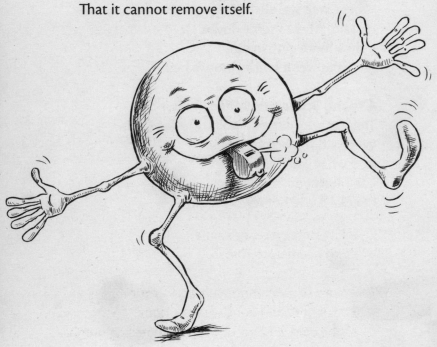

3. What has eyes, but it cannot see
And a tongue but it cannot talk?
Sounds as if it has a soul,
Is a foot long and helps you to walk.

4. What falls more in winter
Than falls in the fall?
And covers the house
In a white overall?
What has a soft landing
Wherever it falls?
What is shaped into people
And rolled into balls?

5. When I am alive, I make no sound.
But, if you pull me from the ground,
To cut off my head is no way to treat me,
I'll make you cry before you eat me.

6. I hold things together.
I've two eyes but no head.
If I'm loose, you can fix me
With needle and thread.

7. We each have four fingers and a thumb,
But of flesh and bone we have none.
In the cold we can stop you from feeling numb.

8. I spend my life in and out of court.
I get caught in a net if I am short.
I am served but never eaten.
Keep hitting me in and you won't get beaten.

9. The maker doesn't want it.
The buyer doesn't use it.
The user doesn't see it.
The director didn't choose it.

10. I'm black and white and waved to show
That there are no more laps to go.
Reach me first and you will be
The winner of the race you see.

What Am I?

1. My first is the place where you stay.
My second is what you do for pay.
My whole stops you going out to play.

2. My first will drive you down the street.
My second's a tame animal you keep.
My whole is where you wipe your feet.

3. My first will unlock a door.
My second is a flat piece of wood.
My whole puts letters at your fingertips.

4. My first comes after day is done.
My second is found in a stable.
My whole will wake you with a fright.

5. My first is found upon your hand.
My second commands a copy from your PC.
My whole makes a unique impression.

6. My first can devour forests with its hot breath.
My second keeps you busy behind counter
or desk.
My whole can explode with a bang.

7. My first is a blanket of wintry white.
My second is the tiniest part of an ocean.
My whole brings brightness in early spring.

FOOTBALL FUNNIES

Best-selling Football Books

Only the Goalie to Beat by Will E. Score.

The Offside Trap Explained by Izzie Onside.

Appealing to the Ref by R. U. Serious.

SENT OFF! by Esau Red.

It's a Knockout by F. A. Cup.

Football Hooligans by U. R. Stupid.

How I Scored the Winner in the Cup Final by U. Wish.

Need a Ticket? by C. A. Tout.

Tales from the Lower Leagues by Carl Isle and Don Caster.

THE FINAL WHISTLE by I. Blewit.

Managers' Quotes

If we played like this every week, we wouldn't
be so inconsistent.

I'm not a believer in luck, but I believe you need it.

The lad got over-excited when he saw the whites
of the goalpost's eyes.

I am a firm believer that if you score one goal,
then the other side will have to score two to win.

The important thing is he shook hands with
us over the phone.

We didn't underestimate them. They were just
a lot better than we thought.

What I said to them at half-time would be
unprintable on the radio.

We have to roll up our sleeves and get our
knees dirty.

As one door closes, another one shuts.

I just wonder what would have happened if
the shirt had been on the other foot.

BO PEEP HAD A TIN OF BEANS

Bo Peep Had a Tin of Beans

Bo Peep had a tin of beans,
Two apples and a plum.
So don't go near,
'Cause I can hear
The rumblings of her tum!

Hickory Dickory Dock

Hickory Dickory Dock
The mouse sighed with despair.
For the sake of this rhyme,
I spend all my time
Running up and down going nowhere.

Peter Passes

Peter Passes lost his glasses.
What do you suppose?
Peter Passes found his glasses
Resting on his nose.

Old King Cole

Old King Cole scored a very fine goal,
A very fine goal scored he.
A TV poll voted King Cole's goal
The best you would ever see.

Headlines from *The Nursery Rhyme Times*

COCK ROBIN MURDER—SPARROW ARRESTED.

Hunt Goes On For Spider That Frightened Miss Muffet.

GEORGIE PORGIE LEAVES GIRLS IN TEARS.

EXCITED COW IN MOON-JUMP.

Farmer's Wife Guilty Of Cruelty To Mice.

OLD WOMAN TOLD SHOE HOME IS OVERCROWDED.

HUMPTY DUMPTY IN INTENSIVE CARE AFTER FALL.

CAT RESCUED FROM DROWNING IN WELL.

MAN-IN-THE-MOON SEEN ON WAY TO NORWICH.

Bird Pecks Off Maid's Nose In Palace Garden.

WHAT A LOT OF NONSENSE

Ladles and Jellyspoons

Ladles and Jellyspoons,
I come before you
To stand behind you
And tell you something
I know nothing about.
Next Thursday
Which is Good Friday
There will be a Mothers' Meeting
For fathers only.
Wear your best clothes
If you haven't any
And if you can come
Please stay at home.
Admission free
Pay at the door.
Take a seat
And sit on the floor.
It makes no difference where you sit
The man in the gallery is sure to spit.

I'm Thor!

The thunder god went for a ride
Upon his favourite filly.
'I'm Thor!' he cried

And the horse replied,
'You forgot your thaddle, thilly!'

Don't Make a Bet with a Yeti
There once was a greedy young yeti
Who had with a friend a bet that he
Could eat at one go, as he sat in the snow,
Twenty-two bowls of spaghetti.
He ate plate after plate, but the more that he ate,
The more he grew clammy and sweaty.
By the twenty-first, he felt he would burst
If he ate one more forkful, but yet he
Gave a weak grin, saying 'I won't give in,'
And ate the last bowl of spaghetti,
Then fell down in the snow, groaning, 'So now
    you know
If you bet, do not bet with a yeti.'

One Fine October Morning
One fine October morning
In September, last July,
The moon lay thick upon the ground,
The snow shone in the sky;
The flowers were singing gaily
And the birds were in full bloom,
I went down to the cellar
To sweep the upstairs room.

ELVISH PRESLEY AND
CLUCKLEBERRY FINN

What are maths teachers' favourite meals?
Takeaways.

What is King Kong's favourite Christmas carol?
Jungle Bells.

What is Dracula's favourite food?
A *necktarine.*

What are a snail's favourite clothes?
A shell suit.

What is a reptile's favourite film?
The Lizard of Oz.

What is a pig's favourite ballet?
Swine Lake.

What is a skeleton's favourite vegetable?
Marrow.

What is an ogre's favourite soft drink?
Lemon and slime.

What is a gnome's favourite place?
Gnome, sweet gnome.

Who is a fairy's favourite singer?
Elvish Presley.

Which is a monster's favourite soap opera?
BeastEnders.

What is a chicken's favourite book?
Cluckleberry Finn.

What is a horse's favourite soap opera?
Neighbours.

What is a bear's favourite pasta?
Tagliateddy.

What is a porcupine's favourite food?
Prickled onions.

What is a kangaroo's favourite computer game?
Mortal Wombat.

HILARIOUS HISTORY

Which queen loved gambling?
Mary Queen of Slots.

Why did Henry VIII have so many wives?
Because he liked to chop and change.

What was James II's first act when he
came to the throne?
Sitting down.

Henry the Second

Henry the Second is generally reckoned
To have been a talented king.
But in *Britain's Got Talent* he found
He was voted out in the first round
Because of the fact
That he couldn't act
And neither could he sing.

Napoleon Bonaparte

Napoleon Bonaparte
Was very unhappy
'Cause the English soldiers
Nicknamed him Nappy.

Julius Caesar

Julius Caesar,
The Roman geezer,
Squashed his wife
With the lemon squeezer.

Sir Francis Drake

Sir Francis Drake
Said, 'It was very much harder
To win at bowls
Than to beat the Armada.'

Richard the Third

Richard the Third said, 'It's absurd
To suggest that I am a liar.'
But he cursed and swore
And ran for the door,
When he saw that his
    pants were on fire.

RIDICULOUSLY ROMANTIC

Two Lovers Stood on Sydney Bridge
Two lovers stood on Sydney Bridge,
Her lips were all a-quiver.
He kissed her
And her leg fell off
And floated down the river.

Mr Kr Sr
She frowned and called him 'Mr'
Because in sport he kr.
And so in spite,
That very night,
That Mr kr sr.

I Love You, I Love You
I love you, I love you,
I love you divine.
Please give me your bubble-gum,
You're *sitting* on mine!

I Wish I Had Your Picture

I wish I had your picture—
It would be very nice,
I'd hang it in the attic
To scare away the mice.

The Old Maiden From Fife

There was an old maiden from Fife
Who had never been kissed in her life;
Along came a cat,
And she said, 'I'll kiss that!'
But the cat answered, 'Not on your life!'

TEASING TONGUE TWISTERS

Can You Imagine…?

Can you imagine
an imaginary menagerie manager
imagining managing
an imaginary menagerie?

Wunwun and Tutu

Wunwun was a racehorse.
Tutu was one too.
Wunwun won one race.
Tutu won one too.

Once Upon a Barren Moor

Once upon a barren moor
There dwelt a bear, also a boar;
The bear could not bear the boar;
The boar thought the bear a bore.
At last the boar could bear no more
The bear that bored him on the moor;
And so one morn the bear he bored—
The bear will bore the boar no more.

Pat and the Pasta

Pat passed the pasta to the pastor
The pastor didn't like pasta so . . .
The pasta was passed to the pastor
And the pastor passed the pasta back to Pat.

Don't Tickle a Thistle

Don't tickle a thistle
Or you'll get in a pickle.
For thistles are prickly
And thistles'll prickle.

ABSURD ALIENS AND RIDICULOUS ROBOTS

Why did the alien land on the roof?
Someone left the landing light on.

Where do astronauts leave their spaceships?
At parking meteors.

How does an alien count to twenty-three?
On its fingers.

What's green and goes boinggg?
An alien on a bungee rope.

What do you call a sad spacecraft?
An unidentified crying object.

What did Saturn say to Mercury?
I'll give you a ring later.

What did the hungry alien say when it
landed on Earth?
Take me to your larder.

What is a robot's favourite type of music?
Heavy metal.

Why did the robot go mad?
Because it had a screw loose.

Why do robots suffer from indigestion?
Because they bolt their food.

What happens if you throw eggs at a robot?
It's eggs-terminated.

WACKY WAITERS AND FOOD TOMFOOLERY

Waiter! Waiter!
Waiter, waiter,
there's a flea in
my soup.
*Tell him to
hop it.*

Waiter, waiter,
there's a fly in the butter.
Yes, sir, it's a butterfly.

Waiter, waiter, this
egg is bad.
*Don't blame me. I only
laid the table.*

Customer: Waiter, I can't eat this soup.
Waiter: I'll fetch the manager, sir.
Customer: Manager, I can't eat this soup.
Manager: Sorry, sir. I'll get the chef.
Customer: Chef, I can't eat this soup.
Chef: What's wrong with it?
Customer: Nothing—I haven't got a spoon.

Customer: Why are there double-yellow
lines around the menu?
Restaurant manager: Because there's No
Waiting here. It's a self-service restaurant.

On Tomato Ketchup
If you do not shake the bottle,
None'll come, and then a lot'll.

DOCTOR, DOCTOR

Nurse: Doctor, doctor, there's an invisible
man in the waiting room.
Doctor: Tell him I can't see him.

Nurse: The next patient says he's got
a split personality.
Doctor: Tell both of them to come in.

Doctor, doctor, I can see into the future.
When did this start happening?
Next Tuesday.

Doctor, doctor, I can't get to sleep.
Sit on the edge of the bed and you'll soon drop off.

Doctor, doctor, I snore so loudly I keep
myself awake.
Have you tried sleeping in another room?

A man went to see the doctor because he
kept bumping into things.
'You need glasses,' said the doctor.
'Will I be able to read with them?' asked the man.
'Yes,' said the doctor.
'That's brilliant!' said the man. 'I didn't know
how to read before.'

Doctor, doctor, I keep getting a pain in my
eye every time I drink a cup of tea.
Have you tried taking the spoon out?

Why did the doctor operate on the book?
To take out its appendix.

Did you hear what happened to the plastic
surgeon who went sunbathing?
He melted.

Doctor Bell
Doctor Bell fell down the well
And broke his collar-bone.
Doctors should attend the sick
And leave the well alone.

ANSWERS TO RIDDLES

Riddle Me a Count
Answer is Dracula

Search Me
1: the letter r; 2: the letter c; 3: the letter a; 4: the letter b; 5: the letter b; 6: the letter o; 7: IC; 8: e because it is always in bed; 9: y because it is always asking questions; 10: DK; 11: the letter e; 12: the letter s.

Riddle Me a Riddle
1: a pea; 2: a bottle; 3: a shoe; 4: snow; 5: an onion; 6: a button; 7: a pair of gloves; 8: a tennis ball; 9: a coffin; 10: a chequered flag.

What Am I?
1: homework; 2: carpet; 3: keyboard; 4: nightmare; 5: fingerprint; 6: firework; 7: snowdrop.